DECISIONAL CAPACITY:
Autonomy vs. Beneficence

ROARING SUN STUDIOS

created by **OMAR MIRZA, DO**

writer **OMAR MIRZA, DO**

art **BEEZZZ STUDIO**

penciler **JC FABUL**

colors **SANTOSH RATH**

finishes **ALONSO ESPINOZA**

letters and design **SAIDA TEMOFONTE**

COPYRIGHT © 2021 by Omar Mirza. All rights reserved. This book or any portion thereof may not be reproduced or used in any manner whatsoever without the express written permission of the publisher except for the use of brief quotations in a book review. All characters and events depicted in this book are entirely fictitious. Any similarity to actual persons or events, living or dead, is purely coincidental.

INTRODUCTION

Requests to evaluate decisional capacity make up to one out of every six consults that a consultation-liaison psychiatrist will encounter.[1] Some estimates place the prevalence of incapacitated patients in the hospital at 40%.[2] Despite the frequency of capacity related incidents, psychiatrists reported an average of 1.5 lectures on the topic in the course of their entire training.[1] It is no wonder that when these psychiatrists were asked to rate their capacity training on a scale from 1-5, with 1 being "poor" and 5 being "excellent" their average rating came to a 2.[1] Reflecting a possible consequence of this educational deficiency, studies have repeatedly found disparities in decisional capacity determinations across providers and situations. [3,4]

Illuminating the long shadows of racism over healthcare is a new clinical interest of mine. The implications of the aforementioned data, when examined with a suggested structural competency model as proposed by Hansen et Metzl, makes the issue of capacity education of critical importance to antiracist healthcare.[5] This, together with my own love for capacity consults and teaching, is the motivation for this graphic medicine text on advanced techniques in capacity consults.

As much as possible, I will reference established literature and combine it with expert opinion to present a comprehensive synthesis of all the knowledge on this subject matter. I have structured the text around the pneumonic *"F.R.E.E. W.I.L.L"* which I use to teach this model of capacity to trainees. The elements contained in *"F.R.E.E"* can all be completed before seeing the patient, while *"W.I.L.L"* references the approach to seeing the patient. I hope that on completion of this text you wil have a strong working knowledge for decision making capacity and increased comfort for clinical situations on the subject matter. I sincerely thank you for supporting this project and taking an interest in my perspective on this important issue.

The C-L PSYCHIATRIST

TABLE OF CONTENTS

FOUNDATIONS page 4
REASON page 17
EVERYONE page 23
EXPECTATIONS page 29

WANT page 32
INVESTIGATE page 38
LISTEN page 45
LOGICAL SOLUTION page 47

 FREE WILL

FOUNDATIONS

Many capacity consults arise due to strict adherence to the ethical principle of beneficence. Inflated by a lack of knowledge around the laws supporting self-determination, this adherence to beneficence creates direct conflict with principles of autonomy. Through fears of violating the physician's Hippocratic oath to "do no harm", physicians will often suspend a patient's spontaneous self-determination in the process of the capacity challenge.

Any capacity challenge must first begin with understanding historical **foundations.** You are probably familiar with the ancient Greek physician Hippocrates, who is often referred to as the "Father of Modern Medicine", and from whom we derive our Hippocratic Oath. In his collection of medical writings entitled "Hippocratic Corpus", he gave us insight into the deep-rooted origins of paternalism within medicine:

Do everything in a calm and orderly manner, concealing most things from the patient while treating him. Give what encouragement is required cheerfully and calmly, diverting his attention from his own circumstance; on one occasion rebuke him harshly and strictly, on another console him with solicitude and attention, revealing nothing of his future and present condition.[6]

This excessively paternalistic approach to the doctor patient relationship persisted well into the 20th century until it was directly challenged in a series of events that are detailed in the pages that follow. Supreme paternalism, when unchecked, paved the way for numerous abuses that occurred in the history of medicine. Its continued influence in healthcare remains the vehicle by which we continue to perpetuate those oppressions today.

Each clinician will be tasked with deciding where they fall on the spectrum of paternalism versus autonomy. Medical education often favors its paternalistic roots. Thus, most clinicians only have superficial exposure to arguments in favor of autonomy. After becoming familiar with landmark cases such as *Schloendorff v. Society New York Hospital 1914, Salgo v. Leland Stanford Jr. University of Board of Trustees 1957, In Re Quinlan 1976, Lane v. Candura 1978, Cruzan v. Director, Missouri Department of Health 1990, The Family Health Care Decisions Act 2010,* and the tragedy of Bruce Tucker, you will see why I have chosen to lean away from paternalism.[7, 8, 9, 10, 11, 12]

As illustrated in the cases that follow, the law repeatedly takes steps to support patient autonomy. In doing so, it acknowledges the great harm that can be enacted on patients when they are confined by strict views of paternalistic beneficence. Paternalism, when combined with bias, can lead to the exploitive horrors that occurred with Bruce Tucker. Thus, it is my position that the anti-racist approach to capacity must view the question as a *"challenge"* to the natural state of autonomy and not the innocuous exploration that *"assessment"* implies.

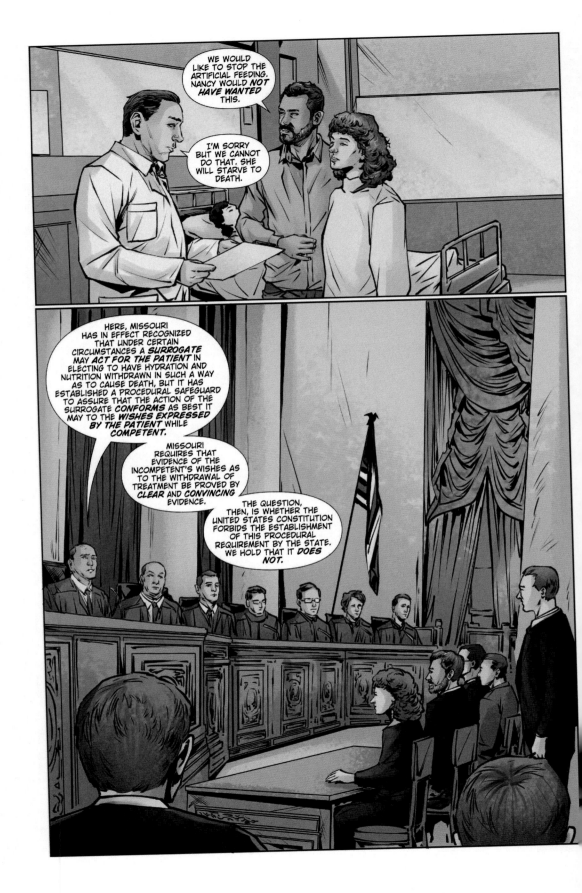

MR. CHAIRPERSON. I REQUEST TIME TO ADDRESS THE FLOOR TO INTRODUCE THE *FAMILY HEALTH CARE DECISIONS ACT.*

Family Health Care Decisions Act.

DEAR COLLEAGUES, I AM PROUD TO INTRODUCE A NEW HEALTH CARE BILL TO GRANT *MEDICAL DECISION MAKING AUTHORITY* TO *LOVED ONES OF INCAPACITATED PATIENTS* WHO DO NOT HAVE A HEALTH CARE PROXY OR CLEAR EVIDENCE OF THEIR TREATMENT WISHES.

I TRUST YOU HAVE HAD TIME TO REVIEW THE BILL, BUT THERE ARE A FEW KEY POINTS I WOULD LIKE TO HIGHLIGHT.

FIRST, *ALL ADULTS* ARE *PRESUMED* TO HAVE *DECISION MAKING CAPACITY* UNLESS DETERMINED OTHERWISE, OR UNLESS THERE HAS BEEN A COURT ORDER.

SECOND, SPECIAL CREDENTIALS ARE REQUIRED FOR PROFESSIONALS DETERMINING THAT PATIENT LACKS CAPACITY AS A RESULT OF *MENTAL ILLNESS* OR *MENTAL RETARDATION.* THESE CREDENTIALS WOULD BE CERTIFICATION IN PSYCHIATRY AND CHILD PSYCHIATRY RESPECTIVELY.

One of the most critical questions to ask when being asked to conduct the capacity challenge is the **reason** for challenging capacity. In most cases, the consulting team will respond by describing some type of patient refusal. However, that refusal alone should not be considered evidence of incapacity.[14] Patient refusal is protected in the patient bill of rights.[15, 16, 17, 18] Exercising the right to refusal should not trigger suspension of that right without evidence for impairment, as most refusals are caused by factors other than incapacity.[14]

Psychiatrists are often drawn into conversations about safety. This focus on safety takes us away from patient-centered treatment of mental illness and towards roles as arbitrators of safety. Capacity is not immune from the ever-present anxiety about safety. When focusing on safety in the capacity assessment, we make the mistake of portraying "dangerousness" as a psychiatric illness.[19] The issues of safety then overshadow the exploration of impairment and lure us back towards paternalistic beneficence at the expense of autonomy. To combat this, it is helpful to be aware of the concept of *dignity of risk* and how overprotection of individuals can be cruel.[20, 21] *Dignity of risk* emphasizes that freedom to make good decisions, without the same freedom to make bad decisions, deprives one of dignity, and therefore a full experience of liberty. Approaching capacity as a means to ensure safety -rather than uphold the unimpaired will of the patient- is the incorrect **reason** for capacity challenge and should be rebuked at the point of consult.

So, what is a good **reason** for the capacity challenge? The truest **reason** for the capacity challenge is when the clinician perceives the patient to be making a *value incongruent* decision that is caused by an impairment. In focusing on value congruence, we center the discussion of capacity on the patient's values. Is the patient making a decision that is in conflict with their long-standing values? Without patient values at the center of the capacity discourse, we are vulnerable to using the clinician's values as the metric for capacity. Secondly, the *incongruence* must be caused by an *impairment*. The *impairment* may include things such as an injury, an illness, or an intoxicant. Without identifying an *impairment*, we risk seeing the patient's values alone as **reason** for incapacity and once again enforcing medical paternalism. This can happen in situations where a patient may be mistrustful of hospitals and prefer to manage their illness with diets or exercise. Minoritized communities with traditional remedies are particularly vulnerable to bias in situations where values are used as a **reason** for incapacity. Therefore, by focusing on *value incongruence* and *impairments* one increases the chances that the capacity challenge will be patient centered, equitable and inclusive.

REASON

ROOSEVELT HOSPITAL.

BZZZ

BEEP
BEEP

BEEP

*"ANY CONSULT STARTS WITH *CLARIFYING* THE QUESTION."

88812

DOCTOR NÚÑEZ RETURNING A PAGE FOR PSYCHIATRY.

HOLD ON, I'M GOING TO PUT YOU ON SPEAKERPHONE WHILE I PULL UP THE CHART.

OKAY, HOW CAN I HELP?

WE ARE CONSULTING YOU FOR CAPACITY.

TELL ME MORE.

*"SOMETIMES THAT'S EASY, OTHER TIMES, NOT SO MUCH."

YES, MY ATTENDING WANTED PSYCH TO SEE THE PATIENT FOR CAPACITY FOR DECISION MAKING.

CAPACITY EVALUATIONS NEED TO BE *DECISION* SPECIFIC...

...BECAUSE IF I AM GOING TO ASK THE PATIENT ABOUT UNDERSTANDING OF THE SITUATION AND THE RISKS OR BENEFITS ASSOCIATED WITH THAT DECISION, I WILL NEED TO HAVE A *SPECIFIC MEDICAL DECISION* TO ASK ABOUT.

RINNG
RINNG
RINNG

DOCTOR NUNEZ.

HI, DOCTOR NUNEZ, IT'S LINDSEY. I JUST GOT OFF THE PHONE WITH YOU ABOUT THE CAPACITY CONSULT.

ONE COMBO, PLEASE.

EXCUSE ME?

SORRY, JUST ORDERING SOME LUNCH. GO AHEAD.

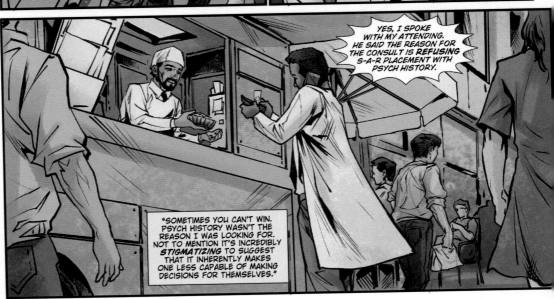

YES, I SPOKE WITH MY ATTENDING. HE SAID THE REASON FOR THE CONSULT IS REFUSING S-A-R PLACEMENT WITH PSYCH HISTORY.

"SOMETIMES YOU CAN'T WIN. PSYCH HISTORY WASN'T THE REASON I WAS LOOKING FOR. NOT TO MENTION IT'S INCREDIBLY STIGMATIZING TO SUGGEST THAT IT INHERENTLY MAKES ONE LESS CAPABLE OF MAKING DECISIONS FOR THEMSELVES."

EVERYONE

After identifying a ***reason*** that is not solely based in refusal, it is crucial to identify **everyone** involved. Much like a game of chess, successful navigation of a capacity challenge requires an ability to play out multiple iterations of the game. In order to do so, you must be aware of each player and envision their various moves in the chess game of capacity.

1) Who is requesting the consult?

In most cases this may be the primary team. In other instances, it may be another consulting team that asks the primary team for the capacity determination. Understanding this is important in identifying the particular person or team from which the concern for capacity originates. One can derive a lot of information from this alone. If the social worker is requesting the capacity challenge, it may be related to questions about disposition. If the consulting surgical team is requesting the capacity consult it may be related to procedural consent or refusal. Identifying the exact person requesting the capacity challenge will help in getting the most accurate information about the origin of capacity concerns.

2) Who is the capacity challenge for?

This may seem obvious, however, in some cases a request may be made to assess the capacity of a family member or surrogate decision maker. Decisional capacity can only be evaluated for the patient. A consulting psychiatrist cannot assess the decision-making capacity for anyone other than the patient.

3) Who are the alternative decision makers?

The alternative decision maker is responsible for making decisions in the event the patient is found not to have capacity. *The Family Health Care Decision Act* lays out an explicit hierarchy of who this may be. Starting with a court appointed guardian, the decisional authority moves to a documented health care proxy and finally to a surrogate decision maker.[13] The surrogate priority begins with the spouse or domestic partner, then adult son or daughter, followed by a parent, then the adult brother or sister, and ends with a close friend.[13] Identification of these persons in advance of the capacity challenge is critical. Data shows that up to 16% of patients in intensive care units, and 3% of nursing home residents have no identifiable alternative decision makers.[22] If the alternative decision maker has not been identified or does not exist, a capacity challenge in a non-emergent situation may not lead to any expedited resolution of the situation. In fact, it may lead to extensive delay as necessitated by seeking a court appointed guardian. Remember, when a patient is incapacitated, the physician does not assume decision making control.[13] Informing the team requesting the consult about this prior to initiating a capacity challenge is a key step in avoiding complications in the capacity challenge.

Hierarchy of Alternative Decision Makers

Guardian
|
Healthcare Proxy
|
Surrogate

Spouse or Domestic Partner
Adult Son or Daughter
Parent
Adult Brother or Sister
Close friend

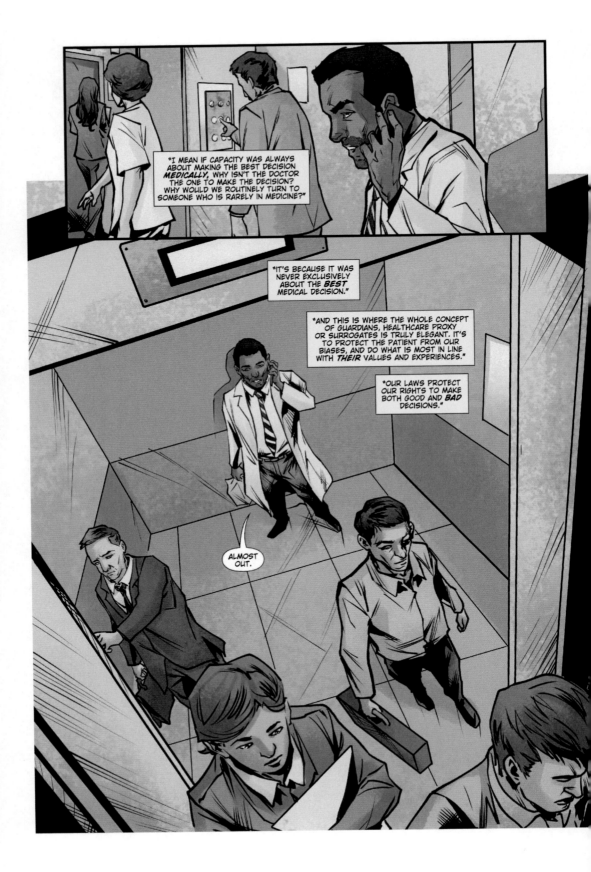

"I MEAN IF CAPACITY WAS ALWAYS ABOUT MAKING THE BEST DECISION *MEDICALLY*, WHY ISN'T THE DOCTOR THE ONE TO MAKE THE DECISION? WHY WOULD WE ROUTINELY TURN TO SOMEONE WHO IS RARELY IN MEDICINE?"

"IT'S BECAUSE IT WAS NEVER EXCLUSIVELY ABOUT THE *BEST* MEDICAL DECISION."

"AND THIS IS WHERE THE WHOLE CONCEPT OF GUARDIANS, HEALTHCARE PROXY OR SURROGATES IS TRULY ELEGANT. IT'S TO PROTECT THE PATIENT FROM OUR BIASES, AND DO WHAT IS MOST IN LINE WITH *THEIR* VALUES AND EXPERIENCES."

"OUR LAWS PROTECT OUR RIGHTS TO MAKE BOTH GOOD AND *BAD* DECISIONS."

ALMOST OUT.

In continuation with the chess analogy, knowing everyone's **expectations** with respect to capacity is much like knowing the next move of your opponent. Many capacity challenges arise through a misalignment of **expectations.** Patients overwhelmingly come to the hospital to feel better. Healthcare workers generally come to work to also make patients feel better. The problem usually arises when **expectations** on how to achieve these identical goals do not match. As a result, probing everyone's **expectations** is a point of intervention to resolve capacity issues before the formal challenge.

Questions to consider regarding expectations:

• What is the team requesting the consult *expecting?*

• How will the outcome of the capacity challenge advance care?

• Is there a situation in which the capacity challenge could harm care?

• Is the capacity challenge being requested for protection against perceived liability?

• What is the patient *expecting?*

• Will the patient agree to the outcome of the capacity challenge?

• What is the alternative decision maker *expecting?*

• Does the alternative decision maker have **expectations** that differ from the patient?

• In which places do the *expectations* of all involved align?

• In which places do the *expectations* of all involved differ?

• How will the alignments or differences of all involved influence care?

• Is there room within the *expectations* for each party to compromise?

Answering these questions brings clarity into the capacity challenge. It will prevent the team requesting the consult from pursuing assaults on autonomy that will not lead to meaningful change in clinical course. For example, when a patient lacks capacity, the treatment team may turn to the alternative decision maker to guide treatment decisions. If that alternative decision maker has already expressed agreement with the patient's decision prior to the challenge, then there is little chance that the capacity challenge will advance care differently. On the contrary, the capacity challenge will accomplish nothing more than sabotaging rapport with the patient by intruding on their autonomy. In this case it may not be worth the risks to patient to complete the challenge.

EXPECTATIONS

WANT

After completing the previous elements *(Foundations, Reason, Everyone, Expectations)* you can take the capacity challenge to a direct evaluation of the patient. The remainder of this text is predicated on the assumption that your patient is conscious and able to engage. Your stance should center around the question of "what do you **want?**". At this time, you may already have a good idea about what the patient **wants,** but the question is designed to build rapport. Prior to your involvement, this patient may have experienced extensive invalidation through repeated requests to explain his or her decisions. Offering an uninterrupted opportunity to express the patient's **wants** can be a very affirming experience. This can be particularly welcome when the patient has felt shamed or gaslit for their **wants.**

You should make intentional effort to avoid convincing the patient of the proposed treatment of the primary team. Especially in cases of refusal, you will often feel compelled to use the capacity challenge as an opportunity to coerce the patient into what the medical team is suggesting. You might feel this is compounded by your own oath to do no harm. However, it is important to remember that discounting patient autonomy is not without its own harm. As the Belmont report highlights, there is also an explicit ethical duty for respect for persons which includes resisting from obstructing their actions.[23] For individuals that come from racialized backgrounds and histories of oppression, the risk for harm is especially relevant. At the end of this text I share a graphic abstract on data that highlights the disproportionate challenges of capacity for racialized minorities.

"THE EASIEST WAY TO DERAIL THIS CONVERSATION WOULD BE TO ASK THE PATIENT THE *RISKS* OF GOING HOME."

"INSTEAD, USING THE DJ KHALED METHOD TO PROBE THE APPELBAUM CRITERIA FOR CAPACITY CAN SALVAGE THE RELATIONSHIP WHILE OBTAINING THE NECESSARY INFORMATION FOR THE CHALLENGE."

WELL, WHAT BROUGHT YOU HERE IN THE FIRST PLACE?

PUFF THE MAGICAL DRAGON...

HA. LET ME TRY THAT AGAIN. WHY DID YOU COME TO THE HOSPITAL?

"THICK SKIN AND A SENSE OF HUMOR ARE ESSENTIAL TO SURVIVING IN PSYCHIATRY."

I PASSED OUT, AND I GUESS MY NEIGHBOR CALLED THE AMBULANCE.

INVESTIGATE

Once you allow the patient to express their unfiltered wants, you can begin to **investigate** for impairments in capacity. A lot is written about theoretical models for assessment of capacity, including numerous standardized instruments.[24,25,26,27] Appelbaum and Grisso propose a four element assessment that includes: understanding, communication of a choice, appreciation, and reasoning.[24] The first task of *understanding* is for the patient to be able to grasp the fundamental information communicated by their physician about the suspected diagnosis, proposed treatment options (including doing nothing), benefits and risks of those proposed treatment options. The second task is for the patient to *appreciate* their condition and the likely consequences of the various treatment options. This is followed by *communication* of a choice that remains consistent over time. Finally, the task of *reasoning* involves demonstration of the rational process of manipulating relevant information to achieve the patient's decision.[24] Only through the demonstration of all these elements does the Appelbaum and Grisso model allow for intact decisional capacity.

Although the Appelbaum and Grisso model was a giant leap forward in standardizing the approach to capacity, it is not without its limitations. In particular, the concrete application of the model could often lead to a rigid approach to dynamic decision making issues. Thus, combining this framework with the proposed sliding scale concept to capacity developed by Roth, one incorporates flexibility into the threshold for capacity. The threshold is adjusted according to the risk-benefit ratio of the decision. Decisions with lower risks may require a less rigid demonstration of the Appelbaum and Grisso criteria than decisions with higher risks.[28]

Grammy award winning producer DJ Khaled is known for many catch phrases made popular by his presence on Snapchat®. One, of particular utility in capacity determinations, is the ever-present persecutory character, "they". A great example of Melanie Klein's bad object, this persecutory projection can be used to establish rapport and aid in the **investigation** of capacity elements. Instead of direct interrogation of the patient's understanding with questions like: "tell me the risks and benefits of the treatment", an evaluator can inquire about what "they" diagnosed the patient with. What do "they" worry about related to this condition? Why are "they" concerned about the patient's decision making? In this format, the examiner and the patient are in alliance to try to understand the concerns of "they" as it relates to the decision. Therefore, the examiner avoids repeating interrogations that have likely already occurred and utilizes the positive split to disarm possible defensive hostility from the patient.

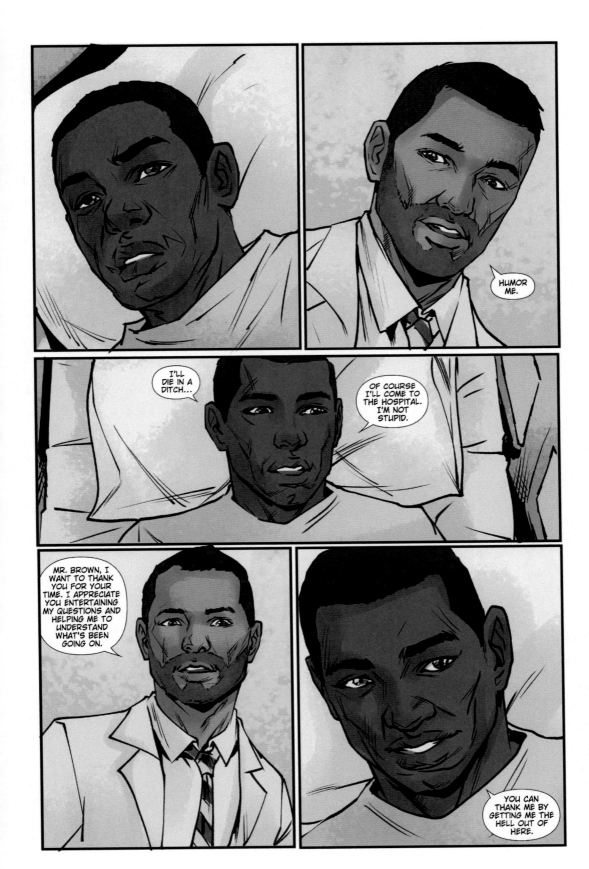

Listening may seem obvious to a psychiatrist, but it is often hard to do. Studies show that clinicians can be poor *listeners* with an average interruption just eleven seconds after eliciting a patient's concerns.[29] Interruptions by the physician can contribute to the invalidation that patients experience when undergoing a capacity challenge and only serve to further the patient's mistrust of clinicians. In contrast, when physicians focus on **listening,** there is a positive correlation with patient perception of autonomy.[30] Therefore, **listening** to your patient will determine the success or failure of your approach to capacity.

Beyond establishing therapeutic rapport, **listening** brings forth the implicit from the explicit. Trying to understand what the patient is telling you beyond just the refusal or acceptance will help you successfully troubleshoot the potential issues. Is the patient fearful because they have never had a surgery before? Is the patient hastily agreeing as a form of avoidance? Has the patient felt uncared for by the medical team? Could the patient be overwhelmed by too much disclosure? Identifying the implicit communications will draw your attention to points of intervention which can lead to shared decision making. When clinicians engage patients with decisional aids, they improve patient knowledge and may improve value congruent decisions.[31]

Potential Implicit Issues to listen for:

- Fear

- Too Much Information

- Environmental Discomfort (temperature, food, cleanliness etc.)

- Mistrust

- Feeling Disrespected

- Alternative Responsibilities (financial, social, professional etc.)

- Feeling Rushed

- Transference

- Avoidance

- Shame or Guilt

- Needing Second Opinions

Capacity challenges are rarely the right answer to the conflicts that arise around decision making. Even after a capacity challenge is completed, you are still left with a human being that may refuse to engage in treatment. How do you enforce oral medication adherence in someone that does not have capacity to refuse HIV medication? What can be done for a patient without capacity to refuse ongoing dialysis? What should be done about someone that is refusing to be discharged to a subacute rehab? These situations are not cured by the capacity challenge. In fact, the capacity challenge puts the treatment team down a path of highly coercive or restrictive measures to deal with the patient. Even with the consent of a healthcare proxy or surrogate, forced treatment over objection cannot be authorized without a court order.[9] So what utility is the declaration of incapacity in this moment? Will it lead to meaningful change that can be practically implemented? What are the costs to therapeutic alliance in the pursuit of a capacity challenge?

Recognizing that capacity challenges often create more problems than they solve, you should use this as the opportunity to compile all the previous steps to reach a **logical solution.** This solution will be based on the implicit factors you listened for in the previous step. In one instance you may engage the patient's family members to persuade the patient into a different course of action. Other times, you might decide the proposed treatment is impractical in the face of staunch patient refusal and ask the medical team to reconsider the treatment proposed. The emphasis here is to use creativity and the information revealed in your encounter to align autonomy and beneficence such that neither is sacrificed.

Originally formulated as the *third option* by Dr. Joseph Yuen, the **logical solution** concludes my *F.R.E.E. W.I.L.L* approach to capacity. It rejects the premise that only two responses exist to the capacity challenge. Instead of only affirming or denying capacity, the clinician is empowered with a *third option* that directs the consulting team's attention towards additional paths of conflict resolution. It acknowledges the reality that capacity challenges are often initiated before all alternatives have been exhausted. If there is not a clear logical solution, the clinician can proceed with commenting on the capacity knowing they did everything possible to preserve autonomy.

LOGICAL SOLUTION

The C-L PSYCHIATRIST

References:

1) Seyfried L, Ryan KA, Kim SY: Assessment of decision-making capacity: views and experiences of consultation psychiatrists. Psychosomatics 2013; 54(2) 115-123

2) Raymont V, Bingley W, Buchanan A, David AS, Hayward P, Wessely S, Hotopf M. Prevalence of mental incapacity in medical inpatients and associated risk factors: cross-sectional study. Lancet. 2004 Oct 16-22;364(9443):1421-7

3) Marson DC, McInturff B, Hawkins I, Bartolucci A, Harrell LE: Consistency of phsyician judgments of capacity to consent in mild Alzheimers Disease. J. Am Geriatr Soc 1997; 45(4) 453-457

4) Armontrout J, Gitlin D, Gutheil T: Do Consultation Psychiatrists, Forensic Psychiatrists, Psychiatry Trainees, and Health Care Lawyers Differ in Opinion on Gray Area Decision-Making Capacity Cases? A Vignette Based Survey. Psychosomatics Journal 2016; 57(5) 472-9

5) Metzl JM, Hansen H. Structural competency: theorizing a new medical engagement with stigma and inequality. Soc Sci Med. 2014;103:126-133

6) Hippocrates, Hippocratic Corpus, Academic Medicine: January 2013 - Volume 88 - Issue 1 - p 80

7) Schloendorff vs Society of New York Hospital, 211 NY 125, 1914;129-130

8) Salgo V (1957) Leland Stanford Jr. Univ. Bd. Trustees. 154 Cal. App. 2d 560, 317 P.2d 170

9) Mcfadden, Robert. "Karen Ann Quinlan, 31, Dies; Focus of '76 Right to Die Case." New York Times, 12 June 1985, pA1.

10) The Supreme Court of New Jersey. In re Quinlan, 355 A.2d 647, 1976

11) Massachusetts. Appeals Court, Middlesex. Lane v. Candura. 26 May 1978. North East Rep Second Ser. 1978

12) Cruzan v. Director, Missouri Department of Health. 497 U.S. 261. U.S. Supreme Court. 1990

13) New York's Family Health Care Decisions Act (FHCDA), NY PHL Article 29-CC (2010)

14) Etchell E, et al. Bioethics for Clinicians: 3. Capacity. Canadian Medical Association Journal 1996 155 (6) 657-660

15) Public Health Law (PHL) 2803(i)(g) Patients' Rights 10NYCRR, Section 405.7

16) Public Health: General Provisions, West's F.S.A, Florida Patient's Patient's Bill of Rights and Responsibilities. 381.026

17) Health Services: Department of Health Services, Texas Administrative Code, Operational Requirements. 133.42

18) Title 22, California Code of Regulations, Patient's Rights 70707

19) Gutheil TG, Duckworth K. The psychiatrist as informed consent technician: a problem for the professions. Bull Menninger Clin. 1992 Winter;56(1):87-94.

20) Perske R. The dignity of risk and the mentally retarded. Ment Retard. 1972 Feb;10(1):24-7. PMID: 5059995.

21) Wolpert J. (1980). The Dignity of Risk. Transactions of the Institute of British Geographers, 5(4), 391-401

22) Weiss B, et al. Medical Decision-Making for Older Adults without Family. J Am Geriatr Soc. 2012; 60(11) 2144-2150

23) Department of Health, Education, and Welfare; National Commission for the Protection of Human Subjects of Biomedical and Behavioral Research. The Belmont Report. Ethical principles and guidelines for the protection of human subjects of research. J Am Coll Dent. 2014 Summer;81(3):4-13

24) Appelbaum PS, Grisso T. Assessing patients' capacities to consent to treatment. N Engl J Med. 1988 Dec 22;319(25):1635-8. doi: 10.1056/NEJM198812223192504. Erratum in: N Engl J Med 1989 Mar 16;320(11):748.

25) Grisso T, Appelbaum PS, Hill-Fotouhi C. The MacCAT-T: a clinical tool to assess patients' capacities to make treatment decisions. Psychiatr Serv. 1997;48:1415- 1419

26) Carney MT, Emmert B, Keefer B. The Bedside Capacity Assessment Tool: Further Development of a Clinical Tool to Assist with a Growing Aging Population with Increased Healthcare Complexities. J Clin Ethics. 2018 Spring;29(1):43-51.

27) Edelstein B. Hopemont Capacity Assessment Interview Manual and Scoring Guide. 1999: Morgantown, W.V.: West Virginia University

28) Roth LH, Meisel A, Lidz CW. Tests of competency to consent to treatment. Am J Psychiatry. 1977 Mar;134(3):279-84. doi: 10.1176/ajp.134.3.279.

29) Singh Ospina, N., Phillips, K.A., Rodriguez-Gutierrez, R. et al. Eliciting the Patient's Agenda- Secondary Analysis of Recorded Clinical Encounters. J Gen Intern Med 34, 36–40 (2019)

30) Pollak K, et. al. Physician Empathy and Listening: Associations with Patient Satisfaction and Autonomy. The Journal of the American Board of Family Medicine. 2011 Nov, 24 (6) 665-672

31) Stacey D, Legare F, Lewis K, et al. Decision aids for people facing health treatment or screening decisions. Cochrane Database Syst Rev. 2017;4:CD001431.

The C-L PSYCHIATRIST

Acknowledgements:

I could not conclude this endeavor without thanking the mentors below. Each have had an immense role in my career. I am forever inspired by their examples and eternally grateful for their mentorship.

Frank Santos, MD
Michael Myers, MD
Amjad Hindi, MD
Ramotse Saunders, MD
Bennett Cohen, MD
Ramaswamy Viswanathan, MD
Alla Ostrovskaya, MD
Alan Tusher, MD
Michael Garrett, MD
Quazi Rahman, MD
Abdelouahed Elmouchtari, MD
Osmond Quiah, MD
Pongsak Huanthaisong, MD
Sabina Singh, MD
Joseph Yuen, MD
Aileen Park, MD

Decisional Capacity and Racism

By Omar Mirza DO, William Garrett MD, Anita Verma MD, Daniel Thomas MD, Jacob Appel MD   Art: Armando Zanker

BACKGROUND

AS THE FIELD OF PSYCHIATRY BEGINS TO REFLECT MORE UPON RACIAL/ETHNIC DISPARITIES IN MENTAL HEALTH CARE, A DEARTH OF LITERATURE EXISTS REGARDING THESE INEQUITIES IN THE ASSESSMENT OF PATIENTS' DECISIONAL CAPACITY.

SUCH ASSESSMENTS, WHILE INTENDED IN THEORY TO PROTECT PATIENT INTEREST, ALSO INHERENTLY CHALLENGE PATIENT AUTONOMY, THUS REQUIRING CAREFUL CONSIDERATION OF CURRENT APPROACHES TO CAPACITY EVALUATION.

METHODS

181 PATIENT CAPACITY CONSULTS REQUESTED OF THE PSYCHIATRY CONSULTATION-LIAISON SERVICE AT AN ACADEMIC TERTIARY CARE MEDICAL CENTER OVER A 2-YEAR PERIOD (2018-2019) WERE REVIEWED. THE RACIAL DISTRIBUTION OF THESE CONSULTS WAS COMPARED TO THE DISTRIBUTION OF 60,707 COMPARABLE HOSPITAL INPATIENT ADMISSIONS OVER THE SAME TIME PERIOD.

RESULTS

CAPACITY CONSULTS WERE PLACED DISPROPORTIONATELY ON BLACK PATIENTS (42.6% OF CONSULTS VS 17.8% OF TOTAL ADMISSIONS) AND HISPANIC PATIENTS (26.1% OF CONSULTS VS 20.5% OF ADMISSIONS) COMPARED TO WHITE AND ASIAN PATIENTS.

RACE / ETHNICITY	CAPACITY QUESTIONS		TOTAL INPATIENT ADMISSIONS	
	PERCENT	NUMBER	PERCENT	NUMBER
WHITE	27.8%	49	53.1%	32, 212
BLACK	42.6%	75	17.8%	10, 827
HISPANIC	26.1%	46	20.5%	12, 448
ASIAN	3.4%	6	8.6%	5, 220

CONCLUSION

SIGNIFICANT RACIAL DISPARITIES WERE OBSERVED AT THE POINT OF CALLING A CAPACITY CONSULT. THESE FINDINGS MAY BRING TO LIGHT BOTH THE POTENTIAL HARMS AND BIASES INTRODUCED WITH BOTH THE INITIAL CHALLENGE TO A PATIENT'S CAPACITY AS WELL AS THE SUBSEQUENT OUTCOMES OF THE CONSULT, AND THUS THE POTENTIAL BALANCE OF RISK VS. BENEFIT, OR UTILITY, OF THESE CONSULTS IN CERTAIN POPULATIONS.

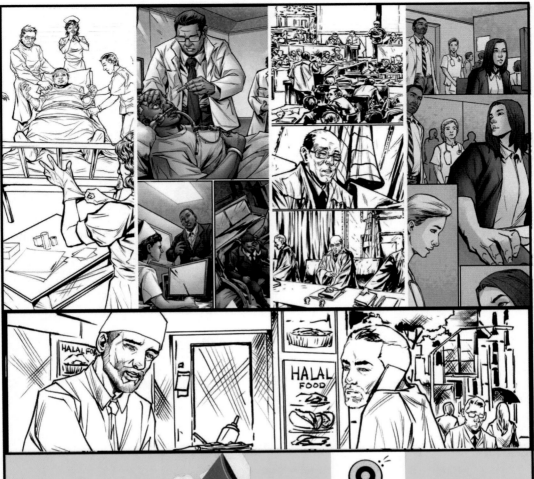

BEEZZZ STUDIO

BEEZZZ STUDIO
OPEN FOR COMMISSIONS

⇒ COMIC BOOKS FULL PACKAGING
(SCRIPT, PENCIL, INK, COLOR, LETTER AND PRINT PDF)

⇒ COMIC BOOKS PENCIL

⇒ COMIC BOOKS INKING

⇒ COMIC BOOKS COLORING

⇒ COMIC BOOKS LETTERING

⇒ COMIC BOOKS COVER ART

⇒ CHILDREN BOOK ILLUSTRATIONS

⇒ CONCEPT ART

⇒ LOGO DESIGN

⇒ WEBSITE DESIGN

⇒ CARTOON ILLUSTRATIONS

⇒ 2D ILLUSTRATIONS

CONTACT US:-
BEEZZZSTUDIO@GMAIL.COM , INFO@BEEZZZSTUDIO.COM
WWW.BEEZZZSTUDIO.COM

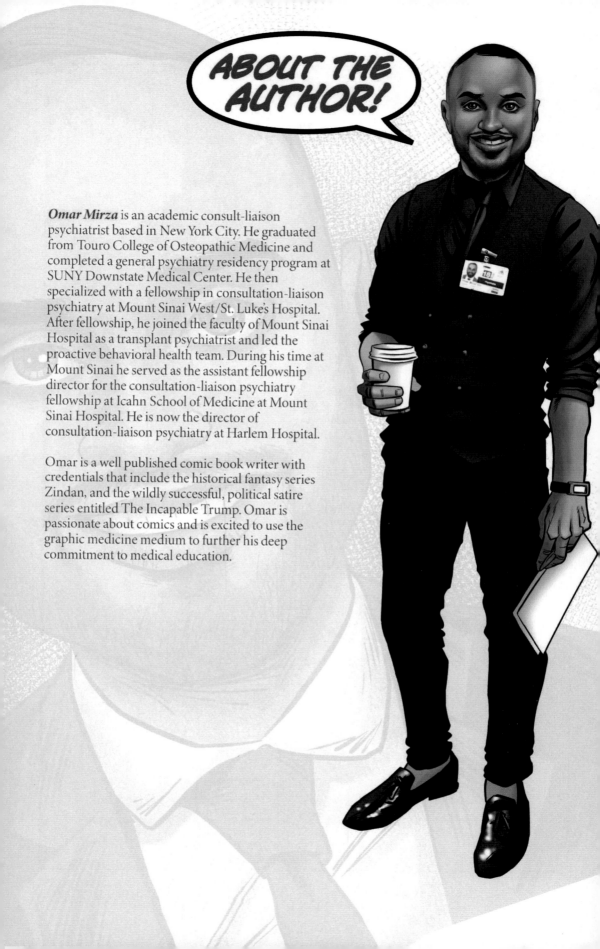

ABOUT THE AUTHOR!

Omar Mirza is an academic consult-liaison psychiatrist based in New York City. He graduated from Touro College of Osteopathic Medicine and completed a general psychiatry residency program at SUNY Downstate Medical Center. He then specialized with a fellowship in consultation-liaison psychiatry at Mount Sinai West/St. Luke's Hospital. After fellowship, he joined the faculty of Mount Sinai Hospital as a transplant psychiatrist and led the proactive behavioral health team. During his time at Mount Sinai he served as the assistant fellowship director for the consultation-liaison psychiatry fellowship at Icahn School of Medicine at Mount Sinai Hospital. He is now the director of consultation-liaison psychiatry at Harlem Hospital.

Omar is a well published comic book writer with credentials that include the historical fantasy series Zindan, and the wildly successful, political satire series entitled The Incapable Trump. Omar is passionate about comics and is excited to use the graphic medicine medium to further his deep commitment to medical education.